It's another Quality Book from CGP

This book is for anyone doing GCSE Mathematics at Foundation Level and working at grades C-D.

It's packed with tricky functional questions designed to make you sweat — because that's the only way you'll get any better.

It's also got some daft bits in to try and make the whole experience at least vaguely entertaining for you.

What CGP is all about

Our sole aim here at CGP is to produce the highest quality books — carefully written, immaculately presented and dangerously close to being funny.

Then we work our socks off to get them out to you — at the cheapest possible prices.

Contents

Published by Coordination Group Publications Ltd.

Editors:
Katie Braid, Rosie Gillham, David Ryan, Jane Towle, Dawn Wright.

Contributors:
Peter Hall, Rosemary Rogers, Karen Rowlands, Helen Waugh.

Proofreading:
Sally Gill, Helena Hayes and Mark Moody.

ISBN: 978 1 84762 515 1

Groovy website: www.cgpbooks.co.uk

Printed by Elanders Ltd, Newcastle upon Tyne.
Jolly bits of clipart from CORELDRAW®

Based on the classic CGP style created by Richard Parsons.

Party

Q1 Sally's mum is making party bags for Sally's birthday party. She needs to make **12 bags**. Each bag should contain the same number of snack size chocolate bars and rubber animals from the packets below.

a) What is the **maximum** number of **chocolate bars** she can put in each bag?

b) What is the **maximum** number of **rubber animals** she can put in each bag?

c) Sally's mum finds that **9** of the rubber animals are faulty and throws them away. How many animals can she **now** put in each party bag?

Q2 Rupert is having a party. He has worked out how much food he needs to buy **per person** and goes to the shop to buy the things that he needs.

For each person
• 3 slices of pizza
• 2 rolls
• 25 g of crisps

Pack of 4 rolls

a) Rupert is expecting **15 people**, including himself, to be at the party. How many **pizzas** does he need to buy?

b) How many **packets of crisps** does he need to buy?

c) The day before the party, **two more people** reply to say that they are coming. Rupert has bought **8 packs of rolls**. Does he have enough for everyone who is coming?

Party

Q3   Jill's friends planned a mini-sports tournament for her birthday BBQ. They split into three teams and played three different games. The rules and results table are shown below.

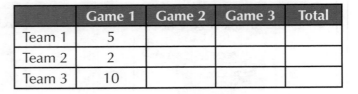

Rules!!!

3 teams will compete against each other in 3 different games.

In each game — 10 points for the winning team, 5 for 2nd place and 2 for the team that comes last.

	Game 1	Game 2	Game 3	Total
Team 1	5			
Team 2	2			
Team 3	10			

a) In game 2, **Team 2 won**, **Team 1** came **second** and **Team 3** came **last**.
Copy and complete the table to show these results.

b) **Team 2** also **won** game 3, with **Team 1** coming **second** again and **Team 3 last**.
Complete your table to show the **overall scores** for the tournament.

c) **Team 1** put in an official protest over the result of **game 3**. They think that they won this game.
Will the **overall result** of the tournament be affected if their appeal is successful?

Q4   Jill cooks pizzas later on in the evening for people who are still hungry. She has four pizzas but her oven can only fit **two at a time**. The cooking instructions are shown below.

Potato pizza
Cooking temperature: 200 °C
Cooking time: 14 mins

Ham and Peanut Pizza
Cook for 13 mins at 180 °C

For best results, oven bake at 180 °C for 20 mins for a perfect squirrel pizza

Classic Cabbage Pizza
Cook at...   180 °C
Cook for...   17 mins

a) Jill puts the ham and peanut pizza and the squirrel pizza in the oven at **10:38 pm**.
What time should she take them out?

b) As soon as there's space in the oven she puts the potato pizza in. As the oven is at 180 °C she decides to **add 3 minutes** to the recommended cooking time. What time is this pizza due out?

c) The cabbage pizza is the last to go into the oven. What's the **earliest** time it could be ready by?

Party

Q5 Chris is throwing a Halloween party and has made fairy cakes of different flavours, shown below. The cakes all look identical. Chris mixes the cakes up and offers them to his guests.

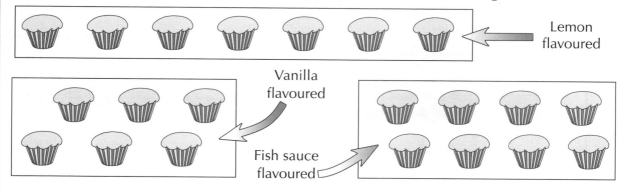

Lemon flavoured

Vanilla flavoured

Fish sauce flavoured

a) Chris offers Ken a cake first. What is the probability he will pick a **fish sauce flavoured** cake?

b) Ken eats a fish sauce flavoured cake. Chris suggests he takes a second cake as he's **highly unlikely** to pick another fishy one. Is Chris correct? Explain your answer.

c) After Ken eats a **second** fish sauce flavoured cake, Chris decides to take a cake for himself. He thinks there's now **less chance** he'll pick a fishy one than when Ken took one. Is he right?

Q6 Ed is hiring the function room at The Ulverston Hotel for his 50th birthday party. He would like to have a **disco** as well as **buffet food** for his guests.

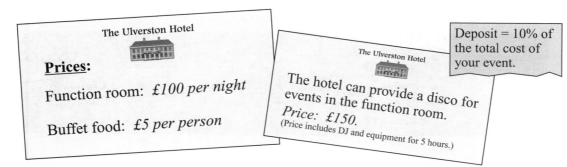

The Ulverston Hotel

Prices:

Function room: *£100 per night*

Buffet food: *£5 per person*

The Ulverston Hotel

The hotel can provide a disco for events in the function room.
Price: £150.
(Price includes DJ and equipment for 5 hours.)

Deposit = 10% of the total cost of your event.

a) Write a **formula** which Ed could use to work out the **total cost** of the party.

b) Ed has a budget of **£500**. What is the largest number of people he could afford to have at the party?

c) Ed expects there to be **40 people** at the party in total. How much will the **deposit** be?

Party

Q7 For Dom's birthday Rachael decides to make him a giant version of his favourite chocolate bar. The original version is shown below.

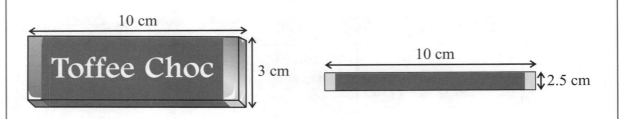

10 cm

Toffee Choc

3 cm

10 cm

2.5 cm

a) Rachael decides to enlarge the chocolate bar by a **scale factor of 5**.
Give the **dimensions** of the enlarged bar.

b) Rachael needs to make a **wrapper** for the enlarged bar.
Sketch a **net** of the wrapper, showing the **minimum** dimensions that the wrapper must be.

c) What **volume** of chocolate does she need to make the enlarged bar? Give your answer in cm³.

Q8 Mark suggests a game of crab wrestling at his party. He needs two teams of four people.

For the teams to be fair, the **mean weights** of the two teams should be the same.

Mark asks everyone for their weight and starts to work out the teams:

Team 1	Team 2	
James — 11 st	Frank — 9 st 4 lbs	Mark — 9st 7 lbs
Cooper — 10 st 5 lbs	Joe — 10 st 11 lbs	Nick — 70 kg
Simon — 13 st 8 lbs	Tim — 86 kg	

1 kg = 2.2 lbs   1 st = 14 lbs

a) Tim and Nick only know their weight in kg. What is their weight in **lbs**?

b) Which team should Mark and Nick each go on, so that the teams are fair?

Holidays

Q1 Lola is planning two snowboarding trips and wants to go where there will be the most snow. She has found graphs of the average daily snowfall each month in two resorts.

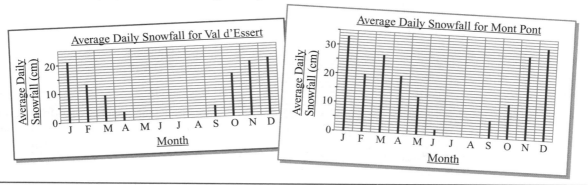

Which resort should she choose for **February's trip**, and which one for **October**? Explain your answer.

Q2 Lola's friend tells her she should take **300 Euros** spending money for a week in Val d'Essert. She looks up the current exchange rate:

> Today's best exchange rate:
>
> **1 Euro = £0.87**

How much spending money does Lola need in **pounds**?

Q3 Lola's suitcase (hold luggage) weighs **19.4 kg**, her snowboard bag weighs **12.5 kg** and her hand luggage weighs **3.2 kg**. She sees the notice below at the airport check-in desk:

> ### Luggage Restrictions
>
> Hold Luggage ≤ 15 kg per bag
> Hand Luggage ≤ 5 kg per person
> Sporting Equipment ≤ 15 kg per item
>
> Any passengers with overweight baggage must report to desk 13.

a) How much does Lola's luggage weigh **in total**?

b) Will she be able to repack her three bags so she is within the weight limit for each?

Holidays

Q4 Phillippa and her friends are deciding when to go on holiday to France.
Phillippa has found the following information for the area they want to visit.

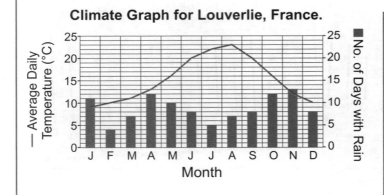

Climate Graph for Louverlie, France.

To: <u>Greta</u>; <u>Dai</u>; <u>Ellie</u>; <u>Marco</u>;
From: <u>Phillippa</u>;
Subject: Our Holiday!

Hi everyone

I've found this weather chart for Louverlie
on the internet. I think we should go in a
month when the average daily temperature
is at least **20 °C**, and when there's the least
chance of rain...

Let me know what you think!
Phillippa x

a) Which months have the right **temperature** for Phillippa and her friends?

b) Which month should they plan their holiday for?

Q5 Mr and Mrs Brown and their two children want to go on holiday next year.
They can either go for **two weeks in April**, or **one week in June**.
The table below shows prices in **£s per adult**.

Number of Nights:	7		14	
Board:	Half	Full	Half	Full
01 Jan — 19 Mar	140	190	200	290
20 Mar — 21 May	180	240	250	330
22 May — 02 July	270	300	360	450
03 July — 10 Sep	330	400	520	630
11 Sep — 26 Nov	230	270	310	420
27 Nov — 31 Dec	270	310	380	470

Child prices
are **half** the
adult price.

a) Is it cheaper for the Browns to go half board for two weeks in April or one week in June?

b) The Browns have a budget of **£950**. Can they afford to go **full board**
for either of the periods they have in mind? If so, which one?

Holidays

Q6 Fiona is looking at a website which shows the cheapest flights each day between any two places.
She wants to fly from Manchester to Berlin, spending **7 nights** in Berlin before flying back.
She can fly out on any day between the **8th and 11th June**.

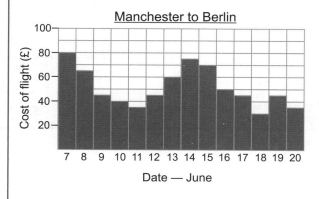

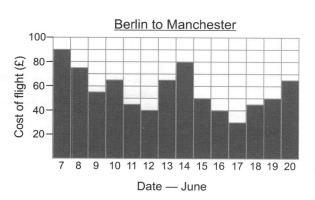

Give the dates of the **cheapest** pair of flights Fiona can book.

Q7 Fiona is flying with Ben from Manchester to Berlin.
Fiona lives in Chorley and Ben lives in Bolton.
They want to meet on the train to the airport, and check in 2 hours before their flight departure.

Trains to Manchester Airport

Lancaster	0747	0926	—	1126
Preston	0807	0945	1004	1145
Chorley	0822	0956	1022	1156
Bolton	0834	1008	1034	1208
Manchester Oxford Road	0852	1023	1052	1223
Manchester Piccadilly	0856	1027	1056	1227
Manchester Airport	0919	1047	1117	1247

```
Your E-Ticket
Flight Details

Flight No.:  BNT3891
Depart. Airport:  MAN
Depart. Time: 1300
Destination: BER

Check-in desks close
45 mins before departure.
```

a) What **time** should Fiona get the train from Chorley?

b) It takes Ben 15 minutes to walk to the train station and 5 minutes to buy his ticket.
What is the **latest time** he can leave the house to catch the right train?

c) Ben misses his train and has to catch the next one.
Will he get to the airport before the check-in desks close?

Holidays

Q8 Will and five of his friends want to stay in a log cabin for two nights (Friday and Saturday) in May. The prices of the log cabins are shown below.

To Do For Walking Weekend:
- Confirm booking and pay for log cabin.
- Email the others about splitting the cost of food and drink (£150 budget for food and drink).
- Clean my walking boots!

Prices Per Cabin Per Night	Elm Cabin (sleeps 3)	Ash Cabin (sleeps 4)	Oak Cabin (sleeps 6)
Jan-May & Sept-Nov (Mon-Thurs)	£70	£100	£120
Jan-May & Sept-Nov (Fri-Sun)	£95	£125	£150
June-Aug & Dec (Any Day)	£180	£200	£220

a) Will is going to pay for the cabin and the food and drink himself, then ask his friends to pay him their share. How much will **each person** owe him?

b) Two people drop out of the trip before Will makes the booking. If the others can only afford to spend **£80 each**, how much should Will allow in total for food and drink?

Q9 Kelly is going surfing and has a choice of flying with three different airlines.
She will be taking **25 kg** of luggage, plus her **surfboard**.
The table below shows the cost of flying with each airline.

Airline	Outward Journey	Return Journey	Taxes (each way)	Luggage (each way)	Sports Equipment (each way)
Surfsup	£26	£23	£15	Weight ≤ 15 kg — £20 Weight > 15 kg — £45	£20 per item
WaveGday	£80	£75	Included	Up to 30 kg free.	£18 per item
FlyBeach	£63	£52	£5	Up to 20 kg free, £3 for each kg over.	£25 per item

a) What is the **least amount** Kelly can spend on flights there and back?

b) Kelly can only afford to spend **£160** in total on her flights.
Suggest how she can fly within her budget.

Transport

Q1 Sophie is a sales representative. She drives to different companies to sell air conditioning units.

The distances to her next five jobs are shown here: She drives to each one in the morning and drives home later that day.

Her employer pays fuel expenses of **22p per mile**.

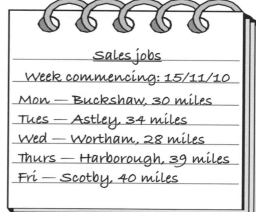

Sales jobs

Week commencing: 15/11/10

Mon — Buckshaw, 30 miles

Tues — Astley, 34 miles

Wed — Wortham, 28 miles

Thurs — Harborough, 39 miles

Fri — Scotby, 40 miles

a) How many **miles** should Sophie claim for at the end of this week?

b) How much **money** should Sophie expect to receive in fuel expenses this week?

c) Sophie has worked out that it costs her **13p per mile** to run her car. After paying this, how much **extra** money does she get in a week when she travels **300 miles**?

Q2 Colin has a job interview in Preston at **11 am**. The office is a **15 minute walk** from the bus station, and he would like to be at the office at least **10 minutes** before his interview starts.

Bus Timetable	Cansdale	08.45	09.00	09.15	09.30	09.45	10.00
	Hine	08.52	09.07	09.22	09.37	09.52	10.07
	Longridge	09.01	09.16	09.31	09.46	10.01	10.16
	Caswall	09.11	09.26	09.41	09.56	10.11	10.26
	Westworth	09.23	09.38	09.53	10.08	10.23	10.38
	Sterne	09.29	09.44	09.59	10.14	10.29	10.44
	Horton	09.45	10.00	10.15	10.30	10.45	11.00
	Preston bus station	09.55	10.10	10.25	10.40	10.55	11.10

a) Which is the latest bus that Colin can catch from **Longridge**?

b) Colin misses this bus and has to get the next one.
Can he still make it in time for the start of his interview?

Transport

Q3 Mark and Rose live in Newcastle. They've booked a holiday abroad flying from Heathrow airport. They're trying to decide whether to drive, fly or get a train from Newcastle to Heathrow.

Drive: 570 mile round trip, uses about 1 and a half tanks of fuel. Costs about £55 to fill a full tank. Parking at the airport costs £76.

Train
Super saver return ticket: £98 per person.

Fly Rapido
Outbound: £29.99
Inbound: £34.99
(per passenger)

a) Which is the **cheapest** transport option for Mark and Rose?

b) Rose remembers that her and Mark both have a railcard which gives them a discount of **1/3** on all train journeys. Which is the cheapest transport option now?

Q4 Caroline lives in Chester. She wants to visit a friend who lives in Dublin. She plans to leave on Friday evening and return on Sunday afternoon. Her travel options are shown below.

Ferries (Journey takes 3h 15 mins)
Holyhead to Dublin
Friday: Departs 19.30 (£26)
Dublin to Holyhead
Sunday: Departs 15.30 (£32)

Flights (Journey takes 55 mins)
Manchester to Dublin
Friday: Departs 19.55 (£32.99)
Dublin to Manchester
Sunday: Departs 18.40 (£35.40)

Trains
Chester
to Manchester Airport
Single costs £14.30, takes 1 hr 9 min.

Chester
to Holyhead
Single costs £20.20,
takes 1 hr 45 min.

a) What is the **earliest** time on Friday evening that Caroline could arrive in Dublin?

b) How much will it cost her to travel **there and back** if she books the **cheapest** option for both the outward and return journey?

c) She decides to travel to Dublin by ferry. If she allows **40 minutes** for checking in at the ferry terminal, what is the **latest time** she can catch a train from Chester?

Transport

Q5 Paul and Simon are going to visit their friend Rhod in Paul's car.
Simon is navigating and trying to work out when they will arrive at Rhod's house.

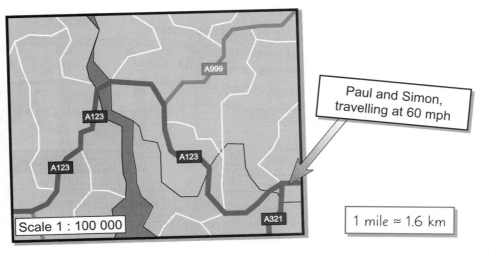

Paul and Simon, travelling at 60 mph

1 mile ≈ 1.6 km

Scale 1 : 100 000

a) Simon measures the distance to Rhod's house on the map. It's about **16 cm** from where he thinks they are now. How far this in **miles**?

b) How **long** should it take them to drive the rest of the journey to Rhod's house, if they travel at the same speed all the way?

But it looked like a road on the map...

Q6 Phil and his family are driving to France for a camping holiday. They will cross the channel at Folkestone, **225 miles** from their house. Phil thinks he will average **50 mph** on the drive, and it will take **35 minutes** to cross the channel to get to Calais, in France.

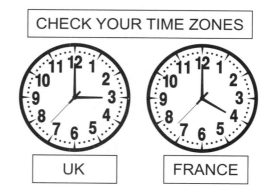

Vive-Le-Campsite

Dear Mr. Fisher,
Thank you for booking your stay at Vive-Le-Campsite. Please note that it will take around 6 hours to drive from Calais to the campsite.
Please let us know what time you expect to arrive.
Regards, M. Poisson.

CHECK YOUR TIME ZONES

UK   FRANCE

a) Phil aims to be in Folkestone no later than **10.30 am** to cross the channel.
What is the **latest time** the family should set off from home?

b) The family start to cross the channel at **10.35 am** (UK time).
What time will it be in France when they arrive at the campsite?

Food and Drink

Q1   Jo is measuring out ingredients to make Carrot and Lentil Soup.
Her scales come with one of each of the following weights: **200 g, 100 g, 50 g, 20 g, 5 g, 1 g**.

Carrot and Lentil Soup
•   600 g carrots
•   170 g lentils
•   150 ml milk

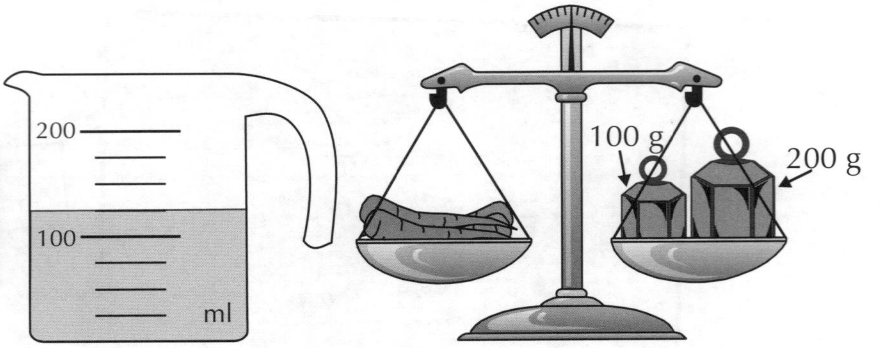

100 g   200 g

a)   What combination of weights should Jo use on her scales to weigh out the **lentils**?

b)   Jo has put four carrots on the scales, as shown above.
Roughly **how many more carrots** will she need to make the soup?

c)   Jo has emptied the milk from an open bottle into her measuring jug, as
shown above. **How much more milk** does she need to add to the jug?

Q2   Andy is making a small fruit cake. He needs to weigh out 6½ oz flour and 4½ oz brown sugar.
He weighs the flour out in a bowl and starts adding sugar to the same bowl.

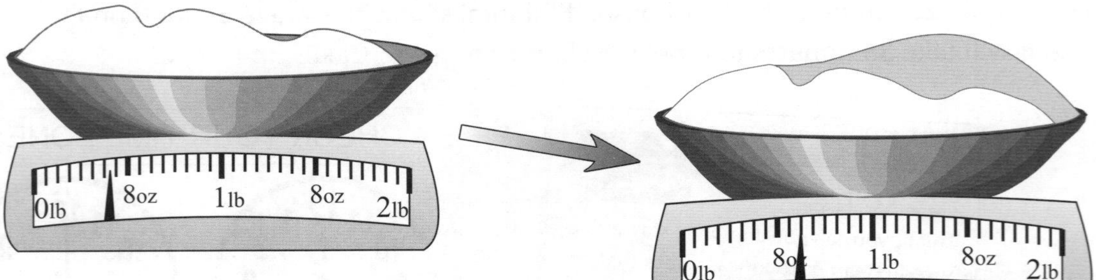

1 lb = 16 oz

a)   Has Andy added the right amount of sugar or does he need more? If so, how much?

b)   Andy also needs to weigh out 5½ oz of butter. What should the scale read
with the right amounts of flour, sugar and butter in the bowl **together**?

c)   Andy has been using a recipe for a large cake and halving the amount of each ingredient. The
large cake requires 1¾ lb of fruit. How much fruit, **in oz**, does Andy need for his small cake?

Food and Drink

Q3 Jake is throwing a party for himself and 23 friends and wants to make some fruit punch.
He asks his grandma for her special secret recipe:

Fruit Punch

3 parts orange juice
2 parts pineapple juice
1 part ginger ale

Mix together all the
ingredients in a large
cauldron by the light
of a full moon.

a) Jake has three 1-litre cartons of orange juice. If he used all of this orange juice, how many litres of **pineapple juice** and **ginger ale** would he need?

b) Jake's biggest container will only hold 3 litres. What quantity of each ingredient should he use to make **exactly 3 litres** of punch?

c) If Jake makes 3 litres of punch, how much will there be for each of the 24 people at the party? Give your answer in **millilitres**.

I've got nobody to take to the party.

Take me, I'm a fun guy...

Is this some kind of joke?

Q4 Jake also wants to make enough of each of the following snacks to serve all 24 people at the party:

Sausage Rolls
(serves 6)

600 g sausage meat
1 small onion
450 g ready-to-roll pastry
1 egg

Cupcakes
(serves 12)

125 g butter
275 g sugar
2 eggs
125 ml milk
200 g flour

Jake **already has** the following:
600 g sugar, 5 small onions,
450 g cheese, 1 litre milk.

Cheesy Biscuits
(serves 8)

100 g flour
100 g butter
100 g cheese
1 egg

Write a shopping list for Jake, showing the amount of **each ingredient** he needs to buy.

Food and Drink

Q7 Chloe and Dan are cooking Sunday dinner for their family.
They want the meal to be ready at **1.30 pm**. To help plan the cooking,
they have noted down how long each part of the meal takes to cook.

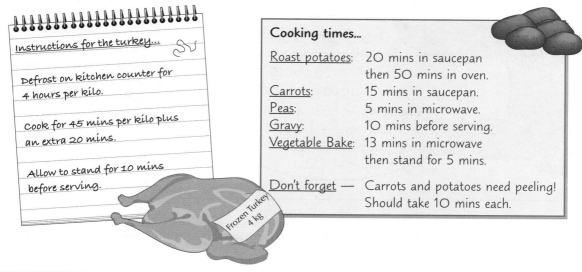

Instructions for the turkey...

Defrost on kitchen counter for
4 hours per kilo.

Cook for 45 mins per kilo plus
an extra 20 mins.

Allow to stand for 10 mins
before serving.

Frozen Turkey 4 kg

Cooking times...

Roast potatoes: 20 mins in saucepan
then 50 mins in oven.

Carrots: 15 mins in saucepan.
Peas: 5 mins in microwave.
Gravy: 10 mins before serving.
Vegetable Bake: 13 mins in microwave
then stand for 5 mins.

Don't forget — Carrots and potatoes need peeling!
Should take 10 mins each.

a) Dan is in charge of the vegetables. What is the **latest time** he can start to peel the potatoes so they're cooked in time for dinner?

b) Dan needs to cook **two things** in the microwave. Suggest the best times to put them in so that they are freshly cooked for dinner.

c) Chloe wants to set an alarm on her phone to remind her to start **defrosting** the turkey. When should she set the alarm for?

Q8 Some of the family like to have milky coffee after dinner.
The coffees should be made with warm milk and black
filter coffee in the ratio 3 : 1.
The black filter coffee is made in a machine
using dry ground coffee beans and hot water
(10 g coffee is used for every 150 ml water).

How much coffee, water and milk is needed to make **five** 240 ml cups of milky coffee?

Day Trip

Q1   Mike and Tina arrive at Mudley Zoo at 10.15. They plan to spend most of the day watching animals being fed. Signs at the entrance show the feeding times and the car park charges.

Daily Feeding Times
Meerkats —12.00
Sea lions — 10.30 and 15.30
Tigers — 10.30 and 14.30
Polar bears — 11.30 and 14.30
Monkeys — 12.30
Penguins — 16.00
Lions — 15.30

Car Park Charges

Up to 2 hours	£2.50
2 – 4 hours	£4.50
4 – 6 hours	£6.00
Over 6 hours	£8.00

a)   In what **order** should Mike and Tina go round the zoo to see all the animals being fed?

b)   When can they stop for a one hour's break without missing any of the feeding times?

c)   They plan to leave the zoo at about **16.30**. How much should they pay for the car park?

Q2   Liam has booked his birthday party at 'Swinging Trees'.
He wants to book a minibus to take everyone there, which will cost **£56**.

Thank you for booking your party at...

The Swinging Trees High Ropes Adventure Course!

Date: Saturday 4th June 2011
Number of places: 8
Course start time: 11 am
(please arrive half an hour early for your safety briefing).
Cost per person: £28

a)   What is the **latest time** they should set off if the journey takes 40 minutes?

b)   How much will the minibus cost **per person** if they split it equally?

c)   Liam's friends say they'll pay for his place on the course between them.
How much will the **whole day** cost each of Liam's friends?

Day Trip

Q3 Wayne is organising a trip to a theme park for himself and two friends, Billy and Ted.
He is looking at the theme park prices online.

Rides £3.50 each.   SCREEEM PARK

All day pass £16.50 per person.
SPECIAL ONLINE OFFER
4 all day passes for the price of 3!

Ride photos £3.20 each.

a) How many rides would they each have to go on to make it worth buying an all day pass?

b) Wayne's brother Joel wants to go too, so Wayne books **four** all days passes using the special online offer. How much money do Billy, Ted and Joel each owe Wayne?

c) Wayne takes **£20** spending money and wants to save around **£6** of it for lunch.
Can he afford to buy **four** ride photos so they have one each?

Q4 Wayne drove everyone to the theme park and paid to park the car.
The 35 mile journey to the theme park used around a **quarter** of a tank of fuel.
It usually costs Wayne **£45** to fill up the tank.

WELCOME TO SCREEEM PARK

← CAR PARK
(£5 ALL DAY)

ENTRANCE →

a) They decide to split the fuel and parking charges **evenly** between them.
How much money should Wayne collect from Billy, Ted and Joel?

b) They leave the theme park at **6.15 pm**. If the motorway is clear on the way back and Wayne drives at **70 mph**, at what time should they arrive home?

Day Trip

Q5   Helen and Nigel have hired bikes for **three hours**, and want to see as many sights as possible on the cycle routes shown on their map. They think they can cycle at an average speed of **10 mph**.

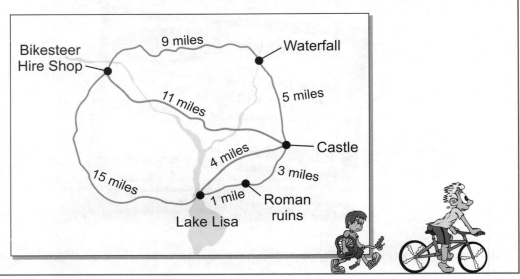

a)   How many **miles** should they be able to cover before they have to return their bikes?

b)   Work out a route that allows them to see as many sights as possible.

Q6   Mia and Deanne are meeting for a day in town. They want to see the **fashion show** at Bedhams Department Store, and be there for the **start** of the 'Quick Flash Sale!'.

They also want to go to the cinema complex (**20 minutes'** walk away from Bedhams) to see a **3D showing** of 'Snow Age' and have **lunch** and a game of **bowling** there too.

The earliest bus to town gets to the bus stop next to Bedhams at **10 am**.

Bedhams Department Store	**Cinema Complex**
Opening hours: 9.00 – 17.30	Opening hours: 10.00 – 22.30
Fashion Show: 10.00 – 11.00	
12.30 – 13.30	Snow Age (3D): 11.30 – 13.30
Quick Flash Sale! starts at 15.30	14.30 – 16.30

a)   Which fashion show and film showing should the girls go to? Explain your answer.

b)   The girls need **one hour** for their bowling game. How long does this leave them for lunch?

Day Trip

Q7 Betty and Claire are planning a day trip along the river, stopping off to visit the **War Museum**, **Art Gallery** and **Science Museum**. Their train arrives and leaves from the War Museum station.

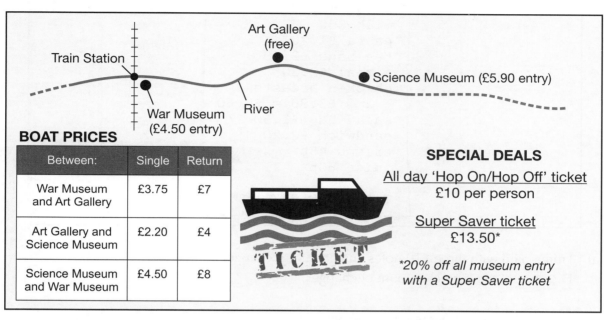

Art Gallery (free)

Train Station

Science Museum (£5.90 entry)

War Museum (£4.50 entry)

River

BOAT PRICES

Between:	Single	Return
War Museum and Art Gallery	£3.75	£7
Art Gallery and Science Museum	£2.20	£4
Science Museum and War Museum	£4.50	£8

SPECIAL DEALS

All day 'Hop On/Hop Off' ticket
£10 per person

Super Saver ticket
£13.50*

*20% off all museum entry with a Super Saver ticket

What is the **lowest amount** Betty and Claire could each pay for their day trip, including boat trips and museum entry?

Q8 Carly, Sam and Tim are at a boating lake for the afternoon.
They each have a budget of **£30** for boat hire, and want to spend as long on the lake as possible.
They want to either hire three individual kayaks, or go out together in a sail boat.

Boat hire

Kayak   £12/hr
Canoe (2 people)   £15/hr
Rowing boat (max. 2 people)   £18/hr
Sail boat (min. 2 people; max. 4 people)   £25/hr
Compulsory buoyancy aid hire
£3 per person per day

Which option would give the three friends the **longest time** on the lake?

Shopping

Q1 Emma has just done her weekly shopping and is checking her receipt.

```
bread £1.20
milk 80p
pasta £1.30
tea bags £2.40
cereal £2.20
chicken breasts
   2 @ £3.80 = £7.60
salad bag £1.50
sandwich £2.20
crisps 45p
juice 60p

Total £20.25
```

a) Emma paid with three £10 notes and got **£9.75** change.
    Did she get the correct amount of change?

b) The chicken breasts were on a '**buy one get one half price**' offer.
    How much should Emma have been charged for the two chicken breasts?

c) The sandwich, crisps and juice should have been on a **£3** meal deal.
    How much has she been **overcharged** for these items?

d) Emma shows her receipt to a cashier and explains she's been overcharged for the chicken
    breasts and the meal deal items. The cashier refunds her **£2.05**. Is this the correct amount?

Q2 John is doing some online shopping and has found three DVDs he wants to buy.
    He has a choice of two companies to buy from:

MooveeWorld:

All DVDs
£11.99 each!

Free P&P on orders over £30
P&P £4.50 to any UK address

Films4everyone:

DVDs
£12.99 each or 3 for £30
P&P £4.50 to any UK address

a) Which company would it be cheapest for John to get the DVDs from?

b) John remembers another **two** DVDs he'd like to buy. Which company is the **cheaper** option now?

Shopping

Q3 Lynn is in charge of refreshments for her hockey match this week.
Her captain has left her a message:

> Hi Lynn,
>   Please can you bring some juice and oranges for half-time? The 11 of us usually have 2 orange quarters each, and get the same for the 11 on the other team too. Could you also bring juice? Just for our team, enough so that we can each fill one of those 500 ml bottles.
>   Thanks, see you at the match!
>   Cath

a) How many **orange quarters** should Lynn prepare for **each team**?

b) How many **oranges** should Lynn buy?

c) How many **litre bottles** of juice should Lynn buy?

Q4 Jenny has two dogs. They each eat $\frac{3}{4}$ tin of dog food a day.
They also each eat 125 g of dry mixer twice a day.

DOG FOOD   TINS each £1.24

DRY MIXER

10 kg bag £25.80

a) How many **tins** of dog food does Jenny need to buy to feed her dogs for one week?

b) How many **days** will the 10 kg bag of dry mixer last?

c) Jenny's neighbour Pete is looking after the dogs while she is on holiday.
How much dog food and dry mixer should Jenny tell Pete to buy to feed the dogs for **2 weeks**?

d) How much **money** does Jenny owe Pete to cover the cost of the food he'll need to buy?

Shopping

Q5 Mel wants to get a new contract for her mobile phone.

On average, she makes 2 hours of calls and sends around 100 texts each month.

She also uses her phone for checking emails and surfing the internet.

		Contract length	Price per month	Inclusive minutes	Inclusive texts	Inclusive data (MB)
Tariff	Economy	12 months	£10.99	100	50	0
	Standard	12 months	£17.99	200	100	0
	Roamer	12 months	£23.99	300	unlimited	unlimited

Additional call charges	Additional text messages	Additional data transfer
15p / min	10p / message	£5.50 / month for unlimited data

Which mobile phone tariff is the **cheapest option** for Mel?

Q6 Alison wants to buy the pair of shoes shown below but she only has **£48** cash. If she opens a store card, she can buy the shoes today and pay for them, plus interest, in one month's time.

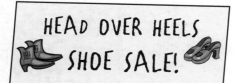

HEAD OVER HEELS SHOE SALE!

5% off any purchase today

OR

open a store card* today and get **10% OFF** any purchase!

* Interest charged at 3% per month.

£70

a) Alison's friend offers to lend her **£15**. Is this enough money for Alison to pay for the shoes **today**?

b) How much will Alison pay **in total** if she opens a store card to buy the shoes?

Shopping

Q7 Paul is trying to work out which washing detergent to buy.
The choices are:

1.5 kg

Whitey Whites

Leaves your clothes sparkly clean!

125 g per wash

New improved

125 g per wash

2 kg

Soapy Suds

eco-wash

28 washing tablets that won't harm the environment

2 per wash

£5.10   £6.28   £6.30

Which detergent is the **best value for money**?

Q8 Syed wants to buy a new carpet for his bedroom, which is 5 metres long by 4 metres wide.
Three stores sell the carpet he wants, as shown below.

LastStock Carpets
End of roll carpet — reduced to just
£160 for the whole roll (6 m by 4 m).

UniPrice Carpets
We don't have sales — our prices are always low!
Our price — £7.99 per square metre.

Carpet Discounts
We've slashed the price of this carpet!
We've taken 50% off the RRP of £19.50/m².
Now we'll give you another 20% off the reduced price!

Which store would give Syed the **best deal**?

Jobs

Q1 Kelly thinks she'd like a career in science. She wants to know how different the salaries are in different science jobs. She looks in a science magazine for the salaries of some science jobs.

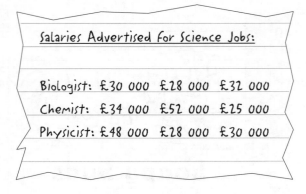

Salaries Advertised for Science Jobs:

Biologist: £30 000   £28 000   £32 000

Chemist: £34 000   £52 000   £25 000

Physicist: £48 000   £28 000   £30 000

a) Which science job has the highest **mean salary**?

b) Which has the smallest **range** of salaries?

c) What is the mean salary of **all** the science jobs Kelly has seen?
Give your answer to the nearest £100.

Q2 Andrea, Ben and Charlie share **£56 a week** for their shared paper round.

Ben delivers the papers on Fridays and Saturdays,
Charlie delivers them on Tuesdays and Sundays,
and Andrea delivers them for the rest of the week.

a) Andrea, Ben and Charlie want to split their pay into a ratio so that they each earn a **fair amount** for the number of days they have worked. What ratio should they use?

b) How much money should Andrea, Ben and Charlie **each** get per week?

c) Charlie gives up his part of the paper round, so Andrea and Ben split his days between them. How much should they **each** earn per week now?

Jobs

Q3 Josh works in a fish & chip shop three evenings a week, from 6 pm until 10 pm. He earns £5.50 an hour and spends £20 a week going out. Josh has started saving money for a holiday.

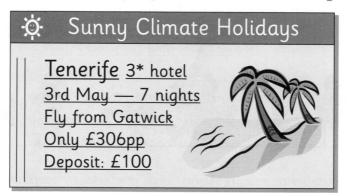

Sunny Climate Holidays

Tenerife 3* hotel
3rd May — 7 nights
Fly from Gatwick
Only £306pp
Deposit: £100

a) How much **money** does Josh **earn** each week?

b) How many **weeks** will it take Josh to save the money for the **deposit**, if he continues to go out with his friends each week?

c) How much money would Josh have to save **each week** to pay the **full cost** of his holiday in **six weeks**?

Q4 Polly is setting up a business providing 5-day fitness courses for groups of up to 20. She wants to work out how much to charge per person.

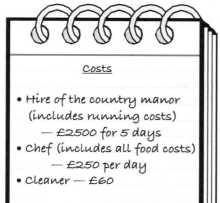

Costs

• Hire of the country manor (includes running costs) — £2500 for 5 days
• Chef (includes all food costs) — £250 per day
• Cleaner — £60

a) How much should Polly charge **each person** in a group of 20 so she can cover her costs?

b) How much **profit** would she make from a group of 20 people if she charged **£240 per person**?

c) Only **14 people** are booked in for one of the courses. They each pay £240. Is it still worth Polly running the course, or will she end up losing money?

Jobs

Q5   Elaine currently earns **£350 a week** as a music teacher.
She wants to set up her own business and teach private lessons instead, charging **£15** per lesson.

a)   What is the **least** number of lessons Elaine needs per week to keep her earnings the same?

b)   In her first four weeks she teaches an average of **25.25 lessons per week**.
How much more money has she earned than she would have done in her previous job?

c)   Elaine wants to earn around **£26 000 per year**, taking 4 weeks holiday. How much should she
charge per lesson, to the nearest 50p, if she continues to teach an average of 25.25 per week?

Q6   Danni works in an outdoors shop. She wants to take a job working as an outdoors instructor,
but it will mean taking a drop in pay to **£16 000** a year.
She needs to earn enough money to cover her monthly rent (£350), bills (£150) and food (£200).

Working out your Income Tax
A Helpful Guide

Your annual salary is taxed at different rates, as shown:

Salary	Income Tax
up to £6475	0% (Tax Free Allowance)
up to £37 400	20% (on anything above £6475)
£37 401 — £150 000	40% (on anything above £37 400)
over £150 000	50% (on anything above £37 400)

E.g. If you earn £20 000 per year, your monthly tax
deduction is 20% of (£20 000 − £6475), split into 12.

a)   How much tax will be deducted from Danni's salary **each month** if she takes the job?

b)   How much will she have **left** each month after tax, and paying her rent, bills and food?

Jobs

Q7 Naz has an NVQ Level 2 qualification in Health and Social Care, and currently earns **£250 a week** working as a carer. If Naz stays in his current job, he is due to get a **5% pay rise**.
If he does the NVQ Level 3 qualification and gets a new job, he'll start on the average wage.

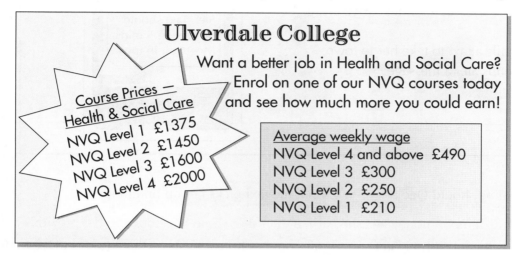

Ulverdale College

Want a better job in Health and Social Care?
Enrol on one of our NVQ courses today
and see how much more you could earn!

Course Prices —
Health & Social Care
NVQ Level 1 £1375
NVQ Level 2 £1450
NVQ Level 3 £1600
NVQ Level 4 £2000

Average weekly wage
NVQ Level 4 and above £490
NVQ Level 3 £300
NVQ Level 2 £250
NVQ Level 1 £210

Naz thinks the extra money he will make in a Level 3 job will cover the expense of the qualification within **6 months**. Is he correct?

Q8 Jennifer is looking at the job description shown below.

Cheeky Chocolate Company

Position: Sales Representative

<u>Job Description</u>: Responsible for selling our chocolates to shops throughout London.

<u>Location</u>: London-based.

<u>Hours of work</u>: Flexible hours, 40 hrs/week.

<u>Basic pay</u>: £12 000 per year
plus a monthly payment of 13% of any sales you make that month over £5000.

<u>Targets:</u> Sales of at least £7600 per month.

How much **money** could Jennifer expect to earn in her **first year**,
if she meets the sales target each month?

Going Out

Q1   Dee is meeting her friend Stef in town.

Stef lives **10 minutes' walk** from town,
and Dee lives **25 minutes' drive** away.

Dee calls a taxi to take her to town,
and sends Stef a message:

20:15   sending...

Stef. Taxi should
be here in 5 mins.
Meet you in town.

send

a)   What time should Dee **arrive in town** if the taxi picks her up on time?

b)   What is the **latest time** Stef can set off from her house so she is there to meet Dee on time?

Q2   Dee and Stef meet Kay in a juice bar.
Kay offers to buy a round of drinks.

She wants a **Passionfruit Punch**,
and Dee and Stef both want **Tutti Frutti**.

Juice Bar Price List	
St Clements:	£3.30
Cranberry Crush:	£2.90
Tutti Frutti:	£3.40
Passionfruit Punch:	£3.15

Kay only has **£10** in her purse. Will this be enough to pay for the drinks?

Q3   The three girls share a taxi back to Dee's house later, and read the cost from the meter:

£24.00

They want to give the driver a tip of **10%**, and split the cost equally between them.

a)   What is the **total amount** the girls should pay?

b)   How much should **each girl** pay?

Going Out

Q4 Paul, Kyle, Tom and Ross are having pizza in town.
They each want at least **6 slices of pizza** and a **drink**.

Pizza and Love Restaurant
Price List

Pizzas (any topping)
Small (6 slices):   £5.50
Medium (8 slices):   £7.50
Large (12 slices):   £9.50

Drinks (free re-fills)
Cordial: £0.40
Mineral Water: £1.00
Fizzy Pop: £1.30

Special Offer Meal Deals:
(Students Only)

1. Two small pizzas
    and any two drinks: £10
2. Three medium pizzas: £18

a) The boys don't think they're allowed the special offers as they're not students.
What is the lowest amount they could pay **without** ordering one of the meal deals?

b) The waitress tells them they **can** order a meal deal.
Which is the cheapest option for the boys to order now?

Q5 After their meal, the four boys ask for the bill.
They want to add a **20% tip**, and split the total between them.

Pizza and Love Restaurant

You were served by: Jemima

Food — £35.80
Drinks — £1.60

Total — £37.40

(Service charge not included)

a) How much do they need to pay in **total**, including the tip, to the nearest 10p?

b) Ross only has ten pounds in cash to pay his share.
How much do **each** of the others need to pay, to the nearest 10p, if they split the rest equally?

Going Out

Q6 Hannah and Wayne are going to watch the film 'Rare Earth Elements' at the cinema on Minsterbury High Street. Hannah lives in Hastwick and Wayne lives in Nauton Green. They are both travelling to the cinema by bus.

Hastwick	1605	1705	1805	Minsterbury Bus Station	1915	2015	2115*
Eastford	1620	1720	1820	Minsterbury High St.	1925	2025	2125
Nauton	1630	1730	1830				
Nauton Green	1635	1735	1835	Minsterbury Castle St.	1930	2030	2130
Minsterbury Castle St.	1650	1750	1850	Nauton Green	1945	2045	2145
Minsterbury High St.	1655	1755	1855	Nauton	1950	2050	2150
				Eastford	2000	2100	2200
Minsterbury Bus Station	1705	1805	1905	Hastwick	2015	2115	2215

*Last Bus

Film Times:

Rare Earth Elements (168 mins*)
Starts: 1800

Snakes on a Coach (154 mins*)
Starts: 1915

Taxidermist (187 mins*)
Starts: 2145

*Plus approx. 20 mins of trailers at start of the screening.

a) What is the latest time Hannah can catch the bus in Hastwick to get to the cinema in time?

b) It takes Wayne 10 minutes to walk to the bus stop in Nauton Green.
What is the **latest time** he can leave his house to catch the same bus as Hannah?

c) Hannah is worried that they will miss the last bus home after the film.
Will they be in time to catch it or should she try to arrange a lift home?

Q7 At the cinema, Hannah and Wayne are buying popcorn and lemonade.
There are different sizes of each available:

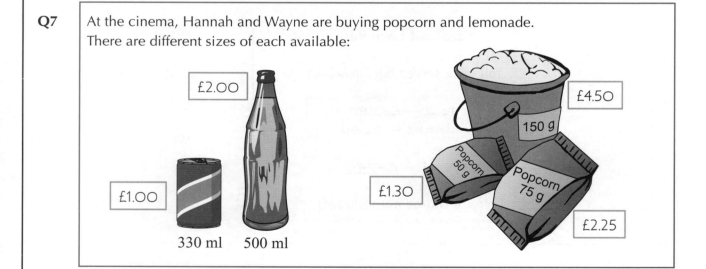

£2.00

£1.00

330 ml   500 ml

£4.50

150 g

Popcorn 50 g

Popcorn 75 g

£1.30

£2.25

a) Which size **lemonade** gives the best value for money?

b) Which size **popcorn** gives the best value for money?

Going Out

Q8 The Robinson family are at the theatre to watch the ballet.

They are two OAPs, four adults, three university students and a 15 year-old.

They are looking at the ticket prices below to work out the cheapest way to get tickets.

Swiss Theatre

What's on: *Duck Pond — The Ballet*

Prices for tonight's show:

	Circle	Stalls
Adult	£30	£35
OAP	£25	£28
Student	£25	£28
Child (under 16)	£15	£17
Group of 5	£135	£155

Special Offer!
Parties of 10 or more get **15% off**!

What is the **lowest total price** the Robinsons can pay for tickets?

Q9 Mr Robinson goes out in the interval to buy one drink for each of the 10 people in the group, and some ice cream tubs to share. He only has a £20 note to pay with.

The prices of drinks and ice creams are shown below.

Cans of Pop

All flavours only £1.50 per can

Ice Cream Tubs

All flavours only £2.50 per tub

a) Write a **formula** that Mr Robinson could use to work out the total cost of drinks and ice creams.

b) **How many** tubs of ice cream can he afford to buy?

Decorating

Q1 Donna has had a new kitchen fitted and needs a new oven.
She looks on the internet to find a suitable one.

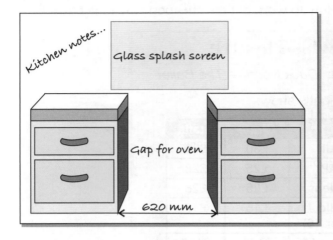

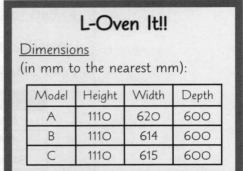

L-Oven It!!

Dimensions
(in mm to the nearest mm):

Model	Height	Width	Depth
A	1110	620	600
B	1110	614	600
C	1110	615	600

a)   The gap for the oven has been measured to the nearest 10 mm. What is the **smallest** it could be?

b)   Work out the **maximum width** of each of the three ovens.

c)   Which of the ovens, if any, could Donna buy to be **sure** it will fit?

Q2 Donna also needs to order a splash screen to go on the wall above the oven.
The dimensions are shown below. The D.I.Y. shop sells glass by area.

75 cm

50 cm

Glass splash screen

Dilwyn's D.I.Y.

Glass Screens Cut to Order!

Any size you like.

We charge £1 per 100 cm².

a)   What **area** of glass does Donna need?

b)   How much should she expect to **pay** for the screen?

Decorating

Q3 Vin wants to decorate his bathroom.
He finds some full tins of white paint, and wants to buy some blue paint to mix with it.

Painting the bathroom...

Area to paint is <u>40 m²</u>

Need in total <u>0.15 litres</u>
per square metre of wall

Mix together blue and
white paint in the ratio:

(1 : 2)

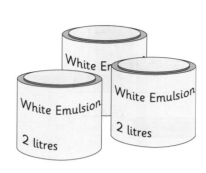

White Emulsion
2 litres

White Emulsion
2 litres

a) How much paint will Vin need **in total** for the room?

b) How much **white paint** will Vin need to use?

c) How many **1 litre** tins of **blue paint** should Vin buy?

Q4 Vin wants to tile part of a wall using some leftover tiles he has found.
He has **20** of each of these two types of tiles:

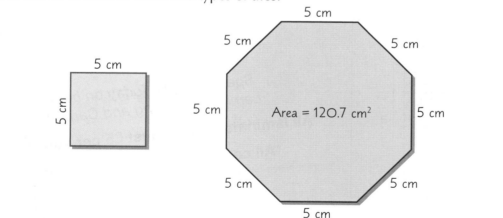

5 cm

5 cm   5 cm   5 cm

5 cm   5 cm

5 cm   Area = 120.7 cm²   5 cm

5 cm   5 cm

5 cm   5 cm   5 cm

5 cm

a) Draw a **sketch** to show how Vin could fit the two types of tile together.

b) What is the **total area** of all of the tiles?

c) If Vin uses all of his tiles, will there be enough to cover a rectangular
part of the wall measuring **one metre long** by **half a metre high**?

Decorating

Q5 Teresa wants to put a wooden picture rail around her living room walls as shown.
The carpenter can make the rail from two different types of wood, at different prices.

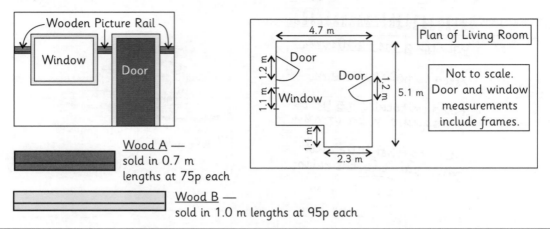

Wood A —
sold in 0.7 m
lengths at 75p each

Wood B —
sold in 1.0 m lengths at 95p each

a) What is the **total length** of picture rail Teresa needs?

b) What is the **least amount** she could spend on the wood for the rail?

Q6 Teresa also wants new flooring for the room. She can choose either **carpet** or **laminate flooring**.

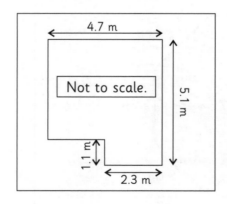

**Top Quality Flooring
at Low Prices**

Special Offers Today on both
Laminate Flooring and Carpet!

All laminate flooring just £5 per square m
All carpet just £8 per square m

a) What **area** of flooring does Teresa need?

b) How much would she **save** by choosing laminate flooring rather than carpet?

<u>*Decorating*</u>

Q7 Hayley wants to wallpaper her bedroom. To help her work out how much she needs, she has sketched front views of the four walls in the room:

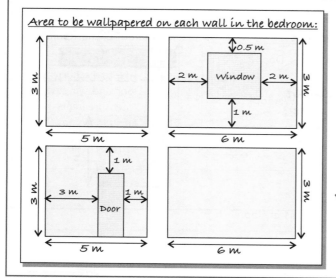

Wallpaper comes in rolls which are 0.5 m wide and 10 m long.

Need a packet of wallpaper paste for every 4 rolls of wallpaper.

Use plain wallpaper — so no pattern to match up!

What is the **minimum** number of rolls of paper and packets of wallpaper paste Hayley needs to wallpaper the whole room?

Q8 Hayley wants to paint the smaller bedroom in her house 'duck egg blue', and paste a paper border around the walls, half way up.

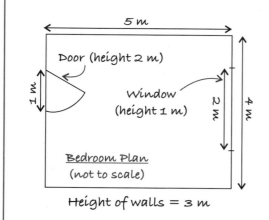

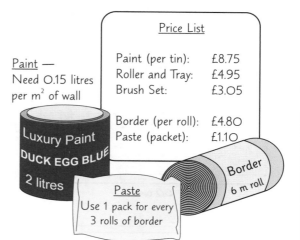

Paint — Need 0.15 litres per m² of wall

Paste — Use 1 pack for every 3 rolls of border

Price List

Paint (per tin):   £8.75
Roller and Tray: £4.95
Brush Set: £3.05

Border (per roll): £4.80
Paste (packet):   £1.10

a) How many **tins** of paint and **rolls** of border will Hayley need to buy?

b) **Estimate** the cost of decorating this room, including buying a roller and tray, a brush set, and enough paste to put up the border.

Gardening

Q1 Aftab is designing a patio to build in his back garden. It is to be made from concrete slabs, surrounded by a low wooden border. A sketch of one of his ideas is shown below.

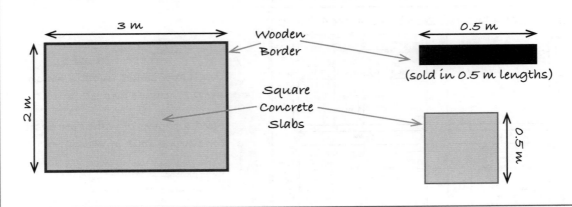

a) What is the **perimeter** of Aftab's patio?

b) How many of the **border lengths** will he need to buy?

c) How many of the **concrete slabs** will he need to buy?

Q2 Aftab has another idea for his patio, this time using rectangular slabs.
His neighbour offers Aftab **20** of the slabs shown below.

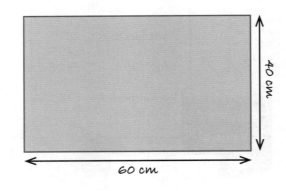

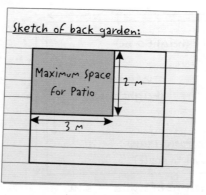

a) Sketch out all the ways that Aftab could arrange the 20 tiles to make a **rectangular** patio to fit in the space available.

b) What is the **smallest total length** of wooden border he would need for a patio made from the 20 rectangular slabs?

Gardening

Q3 Helena has bought some liquid lawn feed to treat the grass on her lawn.
The amount of lawn feed she has to use depends on the area of the lawn.

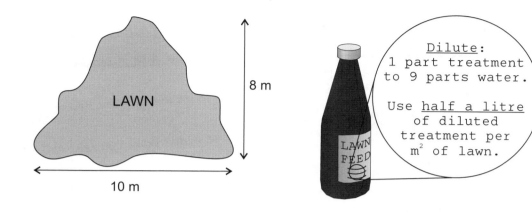

LAWN

8 m

10 m

Dilute: 1 part treatment to 9 parts water.

Use _half a litre_ of diluted treatment per m² of lawn.

LAWN FEED

a) **Estimate** the area of Helena's lawn.

b) How much of the **diluted** treatment does she need to treat the lawn?

Feed me Seymour!

c) How much of the **undiluted** treatment does she need to treat the lawn?

Q4 Jordan is laying some turf in his garden.
He has prepared the area shown below, and needs to order the turf.

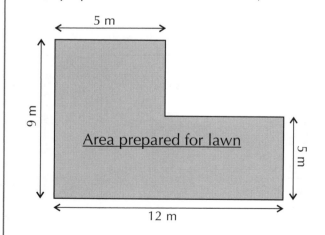

5 m

9 m

Area prepared for lawn

5 m

12 m

Turf Shack

We sell turf by the roll, and deliver _anywhere_ in the UK!

Price per roll: £4.75
(1 m by 5 m)

Delivery Charges:

Under 10 rolls:	£9.25
10-20 rolls:	£14.25
Over 20 rolls:	£19.25

a) How many rolls of turf does Jordan need to order?

b) **Estimate** the price of his order, including the delivery charge.

Gardening

Q5 Sarah wants to plant a tree in her garden.
She needs to draw out a plan so she knows where she can plant it safely.

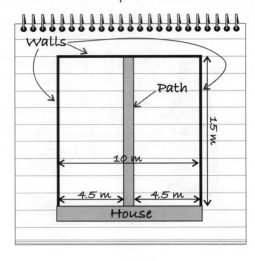

Tree should be at least:

5 m away from house

2 m away from garden walls

1 m away from path

a) Draw a **plan** of Sarah's garden, using a scale of 1 cm : 1 m.

b) **Shade** on the plan the areas where Sarah could plant the tree.

Q6 Cathy wants to know how big she can make a flowerbed in her garden.
She needs to make sure it can't be reached by her dog tied to its kennel by a **4.5 m rope**.

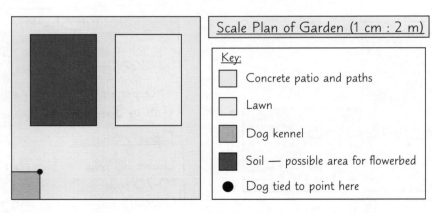

Scale Plan of Garden (1 cm : 2 m)

Key:
- Concrete patio and paths
- Lawn
- Dog kennel
- Soil — possible area for flowerbed
- ● Dog tied to point here

a) Show on a scale plan the biggest possible **rectangular** flowerbed Cathy can make.

b) What **length** of wooden border will Cathy need if she makes this flower bed?

Gardening

Q7 Harry is building a circular pond in his garden.
He wants to buy some decorative tiles to make a border around the pond, as shown:

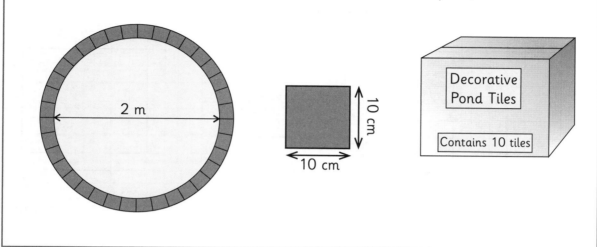

2 m

10 cm
10 cm

Decorative
Pond Tiles

Contains 10 tiles

How many **boxes** of tiles should Harry order for the pond border?

Q8 Harry wants to buy some fish for his pond.
The number of fish he is allowed depends on the size of the pond.

2 m

1 m

...en buying a
...umber of fish, a...
...for a maximum of
2 fish per m^3.
This will give the...
...nough space an...
...en in the...

What is the **maximum** number of fish Harry can have in his pond?

City Planning

Q1 Craig is planning a new office building. The outer walls of the building will be made from panes of glass, which cost **£25 per m²**. The building will have six floors, each 3 m high. Craig has drawn plan views of his three ideas.

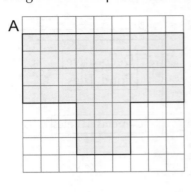
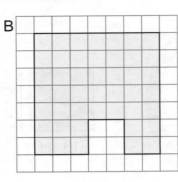
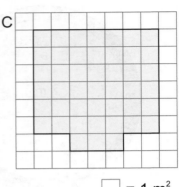

☐ = 1 m²

a) Which design uses the **least** amount of glass?

b) How much will it **cost** to buy the glass needed to build the cheapest building design?

Q2 Craig has modified his design and has drawn a sketch of the new office block. He is displaying the plans in the town hall to propose the idea to residents.

From: Peter Bracknall
To: Craig Steffon
Subject: New building design

Hi Craig,

Please can you draw the plans using a scale of 1 : 1000? Sue's confirmed the height is 60 m. Come by my office when you're done.

Thanks,
Peter

40 m

20 m

20 m

FRONT

50 m

80 m

a) Draw the **front elevation, side elevation** and **plan view** of the office block.

b) How many 1 m² panes of glass will be needed for the **front** of the building.

City Planning

Q3 Planners want to build a bypass to avoid traffic congestion in Sheepston.

> Too many vehicles driving through Sheepston — 15 000 a day on average!
>
> Join our petition for a bypass by

Item no. 3 Sheepston Bypass

Road construction: estimated cost £35 million.

Proposed reduction in traffic: statistics suggest it will reduce traffic though Sheepston by an average of 80%.

Toll road: Vehicles will be charged £3 to use the bypass.

a) Work out the average number of vehicles that would pass through Sheepston each **day** if the bypass were built.

b) On average, how much **money** would be made in toll road fees in one day?

c) Approximately how many **years** would it take for the toll charge to pay for the building of the bypass?

Q4 Following the building of the Sheepston Bypass, the planners want to know if it has been successful in reducing the 15 000 vehicles driving through Sheepston per day. They took a survey of the number of vehicles passing through the town in one week:

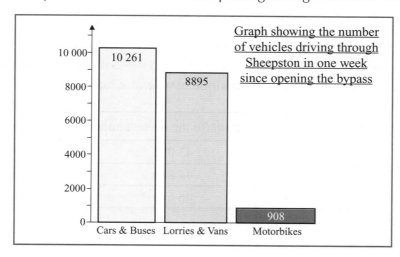

Graph showing the number of vehicles driving through Sheepston in one week since opening the bypass

a) How many vehicles drive through Sheepston on average **each day** now that the bypass is open?

b) Has the target of an **80% reduction** in traffic driving through Sheepston been met?

c) Suggest **one** way the survey could have been improved to make it more accurate.

City Planning

Q5 Since 2005, the New Housing Planning Committee has had a target of 1 in every 5 new houses built in Cheddarville to be classed as 'low cost' housing.

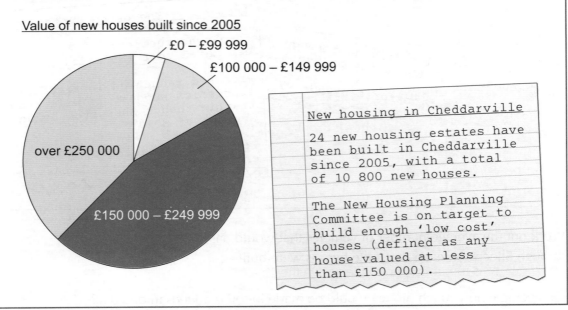

Value of new houses built since 2005

£0 – £99 999

£100 000 – £149 999

over £250 000

£150 000 – £249 999

New housing in Cheddarville

24 new housing estates have been built in Cheddarville since 2005, with a total of 10 800 new houses.

The New Housing Planning Committee is on target to build enough 'low cost' houses (defined as any house valued at less than £150 000).

a) Are the New Housing Committee correct in saying that they are on target?

b) **1500** new houses are going to be built. How many of these need to be 'low cost' so that the committee are on target for **all** houses built since 2005.

Q6 Alex works for the New Housing Planning Committee. He is drawing up a long-term plan for the number of new housing estates needed by looking at the population trends in Cheddarville. The growth in population is predicted to continue at a similar rate in the future.

Year	Population (to the nearest hundred)
2000	43 000
2005	44 800
2010	46 600

a) Estimate the population of Cheddarville in **2015**.

b) Estimate the population of Cheddarville in **2060**.

City Planning

Q7 The side entrance to the city library has five steps, each 15 cm high and 40 cm deep.
The library manager wants to improve access by putting a ramp over the steps.

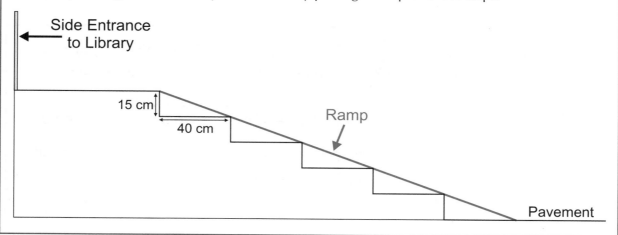

a) What **height** is the library entrance above the pavement?

b) Work out the **length** the ramp should be, to the nearest cm.

Q8 As part of the library renovations, the car park is being resurfaced with tarmac.
The car park measures 10 m by 25 m.

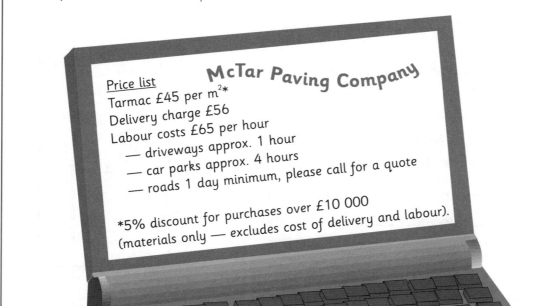

How much will it cost to resurface the library car park?

Paying Bills

Q1   Tim receives a gas bill every 3 months.
His four previous gas payments and part of a new promotional leaflet are shown below.

2009 payments
Jan – Mar _£195.62_
Apr – Jun _£102.48_
Jul – Sep _£85.80_
Oct – Dec _£156.22_

WHY NOT **SAVE MONEY** AND
PAY BY DIRECT DEBIT* INSTEAD?

Save 5% on your bills!
No need to send cheques in the post any more!

*Direct debit charged at your average usage per month.

Just fill out your bank details below:

a)   How much money did Tim spend **in total** on gas in 2009?

b)   How much did Tim pay on **average** each month for gas?

c)   If Tim chooses to pay by direct debit, how much money will he pay **each month**?

Q2   Derek is investigating whether it is worth installing solar panels on his house.
He has got a quote for the installation cost and the average energy savings.

Solar panels — save money AND save the planet!

Solar panel installation — £12 000.
Government grant available — £3500.
Save up to £610 a year on your electricity bill.

Reduce your electricity bills the green way!

What is the **minimum** number of years it will take Derek
to get back the cost of installing solar panels?

Paying Bills

Q3 Tim has just had a water meter installed in his house.

This means that instead of paying a fixed price of **£198 a year** for water, he will now only be charged for the water he uses.

The graph shows how much he'll be charged:

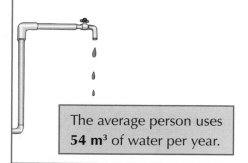

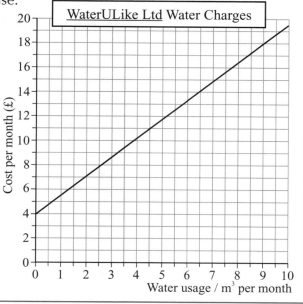

The average person uses **54 m³** of water per year.

a) Estimate Tim's **annual** water bill, if he uses an average amount of water each month.

b) Tim's girlfriend plans to move in with him. Will it be cheaper for Tim to **keep** the water meter or **switch** back to paying the fixed price? Explain your answer.

Q4 Anna receives a bill based on an estimate of how much electricity she's used.
She takes a meter reading and discovers she's only used **478** units.

UTILITIES

```
                              Anna Watkins
                              9 Sparkie Avenue
                              Lecton
                              LE8 2PT

                              01/04/11

Bill

Estimated usage:                   512 units
325 units @ 16p per unit           £52.00
Remaining units @ 11p per unit     £20.57
                                   _____
Total                              £72.57
   + VAT @ 5%                      £76.20
```

How much has Anna been **overcharged** by the electricity company?

Paying Bills

Q5 Lucy is having a party to celebrate her 21ˢᵗ birthday. She has already paid a **£200** deposit and must pay **half the remaining amount** six weeks before her party.
She has received the invoice shown below.

Hotel Superior

INVOICE: Lucy Jones
Party: 12ᵗʰ June 2010

Venue hire	£250
Buffet meal	
50 people @ £12.99 each	£779.40
Total	£1029.40
+VAT @17.5%	£1209.55
Less deposit	− £200
	£1009.55

Please pay £504.78 by 1ˢᵗ May.

a) The cost is higher than Lucy was expecting. How much has she been **overcharged** for the buffet?

b) What is the correct amount that Lucy has to pay by the **1st May**?

Q6 Steve has signed up for a new internet deal.
He has chosen the **18 month** contract shown below.

12 month contract*
£5.99 for the first 3 months,
then £14.99 per month.

18 month contract*
£5.99 for the first 3 months,
then £12.99 per month.

No minimum term
£14.99 per month.

*If you pay by direct debit, the total cost will be averaged out over the length of your contract.

Steve pays **quarterly** by direct debit. He notices that **£35.47** has been taken out of his bank account after three months. Has Steve been put on the correct contract?

Paying Bills

Q7 Jane usually spends about £32 a month on her mobile phone bill.

She wants to try to reduce her bill to under £25 a month by switching to a different tariff.

Bill date: May 2010

Your tariff: TalkyTalk — £17.01
Additional 116 messages @ 9p/msg — £10.44
Total before VAT — £27.45
VAT at 17.5% — £4.80
Total — **£32.25**

This month you have used **90** of your 500 inclusive minutes and **100** of your 100 inclusive messages.

		Inclusive calls per month	Inclusive texts per month	Monthly cost (before VAT*)	Additional charges (before VAT*)
TARIFF	TextyText	30 minutes	250 messages	£12.76	Calls 17p/min
	TextyTalk	150 minutes	150 messages	£16.16	
	TextyTalkPlus	200 minutes	200 messages	£17.86	Texts 9p/msg

* VAT charged at 17.5%

Based on her bill for May, which tariff should Jane be on to reduce her bill to **under £25**?

Q8 Tracy bought a second-hand car in 2008 for £995. The car's value falls by 10% each year Tracy has it. Two years after she bought it, the car failed its MOT. The repair costs are shown below.

```
PRICE LIST

Parts:
 Radiator            £195
 Brakes              £75
 Exhaust             £85
 Tyres (set of 4)    £210
 Oil service         £35
Labour charge        £95

VAT is charged at 17.5%
of the total.
```

Did Tracy **pay more** to fix her car than the car was worth in 2010? Explain your answer.

In the News

Q1 On the Newzcrunch website, there is an article about the results of an online poll.
Courtney is thinking about using the article as evidence for a school essay on 'popular culture'.

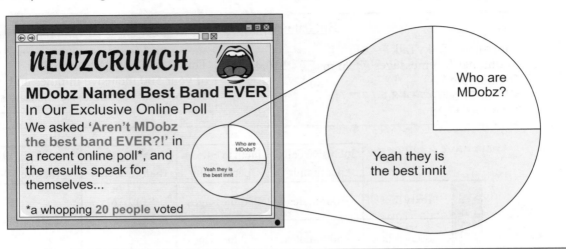

a) What **percentage** of people who voted in the poll said MDobz were the best?

b) How **many people** said they were the best?

c) Courtney thinks the article might not be a very reliable study to use for her essay.
Give **two reasons** why the results of the poll might be unreliable.

Q2 Rubi looks in the 'classified' adverts in the newspaper at houses for sale
in Udderston and Trundle.

Property in Trundle

3 bed Semi	£120 000
1 bed Flat	£90 000
2 bed Terraced	£100 000
1 bed Flat	£95 000
2 bed Terraced	£110 000
3 bed Terraced	£115 000
4 bed Detached	£345 000
3 bed Detached	£122 000
4 bed Semi	£130 000
2 bed Flat	£98 000

Property in Udderston

2 bed Flat	£75 000
1 bed Flat	£60 000
3 bed Detached	£160 000
2 bed Terraced	£95 000
Studio Apartment	£54 000
2 bed Semi	£120 000
3 bed Terraced	£125 000
5 bed Detached	£290 000
3 bed Semi	£155 000
4 bed Semi	£165 000

a) Which area has the highest **median** house price?

b) Which area has the highest **mean** house price?

c) Why might Rubi find it more reliable to use the **median**
rather than the mean to find the average price in Trundle?

In the News

Q3 Vikram is a journalist investigating levels of unemployment for his local newspaper.
He is planning to carry out a survey in the town and write about his findings.

Ideas for Survey:

— Stand outside job centre in town

— Tuesday, around 11am?

— Ask about 10 people whether they have a job or not...

— Put the results in a graph and have the article ready for Wednesday's front page!

Think I'll include these graphs too as they show that we had twice as many people unemployed as Big City last year...

Employed

Unemployed

Big City   Localville
Unemployment Levels Last Year

a) Explain **two changes** Vikram could make to his survey to make his results more reliable.

b) Explain why Vikram could be **wrong** about what the graphs show.

Q4 Vikram has also drafted an article about the local wildlife:

Local News

Inside: All the sporting news

Giant Toad Invasion

Giant Toads Outnumber Normal Toads in Town Park

Giant Toads Outnumber Normal Toads in Town Park

An experiment was carried out to monitor the extent of the invasion.
This chart shows how many of the toads in the park are 'giant' compared to 'normal':

Number in Park

Normal

Giant

a) Why might Vikram's bar chart be **misleading**?

b) Vikram's boss thinks it would be better to display the information as a **pie chart**.
Draw a pie chart that he could use to accurately display the data.

In the News

Q5 Ken presents a sports radio programme. Today is the final match in the National Staring Contest, and Ken needs to talk about who he thinks has the best chance of winning.

Contender A: 'Eyes' McGregor
Past Performance:

Opponent	Result	Stare Time (mins to nearest min)
Redeye Robson	Won	26
Laura Lashes	Lost	42
Wide-eye Will	Won	97
Max Stare	Lost	13
Bob Blinky	Won	30
Carol Cornea	Won	11
Phil Focus	Lost	54
Retinal Ryan	Won	88
Starey Simpson	Won	35
Mary Myopia	Won	49

Contender B: Arthur 'The Unblinkable'
Past Performance:

Opponent	Result	Stare Time (mins to nearest min)
Carol Cornea	Won	55
Mary Myopia	Won	72
Retinal Ryan	Lost	94
Max Stare	Lost	19
Laura Lashes	Won	45

a) 'Eyes' McGregor is the favourite. Based on his past results, what is the probability he will **win**?

b) In the case of a draw, the winner will be the contender with the highest **mean** stare time from the previous matches. Who would this be?

Q6 Ken has been asked to look into the performance of the top three 'head-the-ball' clubs in the league, who have all finished on the same number of points. He has to choose who has the **highest average goal difference**, and who has the **most consistent results**.

Team	Goal Difference in all 20 League Matches																			
Nutters Utd	-2	+4	+1	0	-1	+6	+1	+1	-1	0	-3	+5	+2	+1	+1	+2	-2	0	+1	-1
Headly Town	+9	-3	+6	-7	0	0	+2	+3	+1	-2	-2	-4	+7	+9	-5	+1	+2	0	+1	+1
Noggin City	+1	-2	+2	+1	0	+3	-1	+1	+1	0	0	-1	+2	+2	+1	-1	+2	-1	+2	-2

Which of the teams should Ken choose for each category? Explain why.

Health and Fitness

Q1 Jane is the manager of a leisure centre. She is concerned that membership levels are falling and wants to know how they can improve. She posted the questionnaire below to all members, but did not get many returned.

> 1. How often do you visit the leisure centre?
> ....
>
> 2. Which leisure facilities do you use here?
> ....
>
> 3. What other facilities would you like us to offer?
> ....

a) What could Jane do to encourage more members to return their questionnaires?

b) Give **one reason** why the responses she **does** get may not be useful to her.

c) **Explain** how the questionnaire could be **re-written** to help Jane get more useful responses.

d) Suggest **two** other ways that Jane could research what people want from a local leisure centre.

Q2 Ribble Rovers are currently second in their netball league and clear of the other teams below. Their final match of the season is against top of the league Duddon Dragons, and will decide which team has the most points and wins the league.

Ribble Rovers

Result	No. of games this season
Won	12
Lost	5
Drew	2

Goal Difference = +9

Duddon Dragons

Result	No. of games this season
Won	13
Lost	4
Drew	2

Goal Difference = +10

Netball League Scoring Rules
- Each team will play 20 matches.
- Points are awarded as follows:
  Win — 3 pts
  Draw — 1 pt
  Lose — 0 pts

If more than one team has the highest number of points at the end of the season, the winner will be the team with the highest goal difference.

a) How many **points** do each of the teams currently have?

b) Ribble Rovers **win** their final match with a score of **4-2**. Is this enough for them to win the league?

Health and Fitness

Q3   Jane is designing a new advert for a leisure centre. She thinks using information about the Body Mass Index (BMI) of some current members may encourage people to join.

Body Mass Index (BMI)	20	21	23	25	15	24	37	28	22	23	25	34
Hours spent exercising at leisure centre per week	10	9	8	7	12	8	3	6	9	9	8	4

a)   Plot a **scatter graph** of members' BMI against the number of hours they exercise each week.

b)   What **relationship** does the graph show between BMI and the time spent exercising each week?

c)   Jane's advert says "Lower your BMI by using our gym — just look at the proof!"
Why might her claim be **incorrect**?

Q4   Clive's personal trainer has asked him to keep a food diary for one typical week, so that she can work out how many training sessions he needs each week to burn off the excess calories he eats.

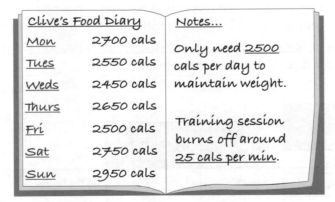

Clive's Food Diary

Mon	2700 cals
Tues	2550 cals
Weds	2450 cals
Thurs	2650 cals
Fri	2500 cals
Sat	2750 cals
Sun	2950 cals

Notes...

Only need <u>2500</u> cals per day to maintain weight.

Training session burns off around <u>25 cals per min</u>.

a)   Calculate the **mean** number of calories that Clive consumes each day.

b)   How many **25 minute** training sessions will Clive need to burn off the excess calories he consumes each week, if his average daily intake stays the same?

Health and Fitness

Q5 Steve has just completed his first 10 km run. He used a stopwatch to keep a record of his time after each kilometre. He's plotted his times on the line graph shown.

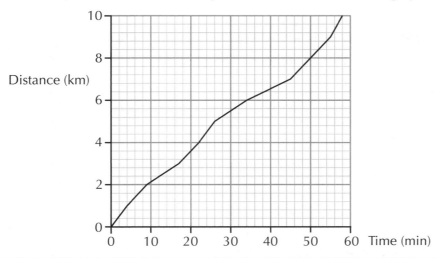

a) Was Steve's **average speed** higher in the first half of the race or in the second half?

b) Steve thinks he has a **strong sprint finish**. How can you tell this from the graph?

c) Steve is running his next 10 km race with a pacemaker, who will set the pace at **12 km/hr** for the whole race. How many **minutes** should it take Steve to finish the race?

Q6 Fred is captain of the local cricket team. He needs to select two more batters for the team. He's listed the number of runs scored by the best four youth cricketers in five different matches.

Cricketer	Number of runs				
	Match 1	Match 2	Match 3	Match 4	Match 5
Mark	59	42	38	61	44
Ryan	56	50	42	58	48
Peter	72	41	49	51	22
Geoff	57	43	44	55	52

a) Fred wants to select the person who has scored the **highest mean** number of runs. Who should Fred select, and what is their average?

b) Fred also wants to select the most **consistent** player. Who should he select?

c) Peter asks Fred not to count his performance in **Match 5** as he was injured. Will doing this affect who Fred selects?

Health and Fitness

Q7 Laura goes swimming at the local leisure centre **twice a week** and uses their gym **once a week**. She buys 'pay as you go' (PAYG) passes each time, but thinks it may be cheaper to pay for membership instead, giving her unlimited use of certain facilities each month.

> ## Leisure Centre
> Prices
>
> <u>PAYG Prices (per session):</u>
> PAYG swim pass — £3.00
> PAYG gym pass — £3.50
>
> <u>Membership Prices (per month):</u>
> Swimming pool membership — £25
> Gym membership — £35
> Combined gym and swimming pool membership — £45

What is the cheapest way for Laura to pay for her swimming pool and gym use over **one year**?

Q8 Brian is a technician at a gym. He has been asked to modify the running machine program to make it more realistic. The graph below shows some results from a real race.

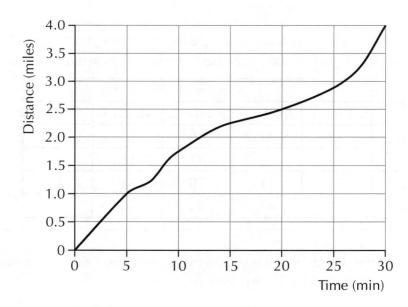

Brian splits the program into **three equal** time sections, each with a speed matching the **average speed** of the real race over these sections. Calculate the required speeds for each section in **mph**.

Car Boot Sale

Q1 Sarah has set up a stall at her local car boot sale. She starts the day with £21.70 in her cash box so that she has change to give to customers. Some of the items she is selling are shown below.

All books and CDs 80p

All soft toys £1.30

£2.50

£1.20

a) A customer buys **2 CDs**, a **scarf** and a **hairdryer**. How much should Sarah charge her?

b) Another customer buys a **book** and a **teddy bear**. He pays with a £10 note. How much **change** should Sarah give him?

c) At the end of the day, Sarah has **£87.50** in her cash box. How much money has she **made**?

Q2 Jonny has £8 to spend. He sees some things he wants to buy, shown below.

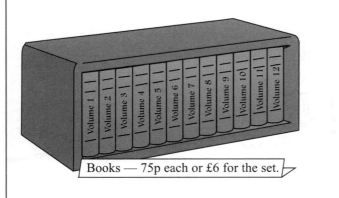

Volume 1 Volume 2 Volume 3 Volume 4 Volume 5 Volume 6 Volume 7 Volume 8 Volume 9 Volume 10 Volume 11 Volume 12

Books — 75p each or £6 for the set.

Badges: 50p
Marbles: 45p
Spinning Tops: 90p

a) Jonny already has **3 books** from the set. Is it cheaper for him to buy **only** the books that he **needs** or to buy the **whole set**?

b) Jonny decides to spend the rest of his money on **marbles**. How many can he afford to buy?

Car Boot Sale

Q3 Dave wants to buy some cushions. Two sellers have cushions that would match his sofa, and both of them have special offers on.

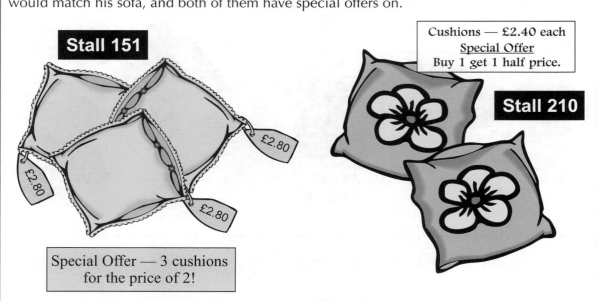

Stall 151

£2.80 £2.80 £2.80

Special Offer — 3 cushions for the price of 2!

Cushions — £2.40 each
Special Offer
Buy 1 get 1 half price.

Stall 210

a) Dave wants to buy **3 cushions** as cheaply as possible. Which stall should he buy them from?

b) Dave remembers that it's his mum's birthday soon and she might like a cushion.
Which stall should he buy the cushions from if he is going to buy an **extra one** for his mum?

c) Dave pays for the four cushions using a £20 note.
He is given **£12.60** change. Is this the right amount?

Q4 Melanie thinks that the prices she is charging, shown below, may be too high.

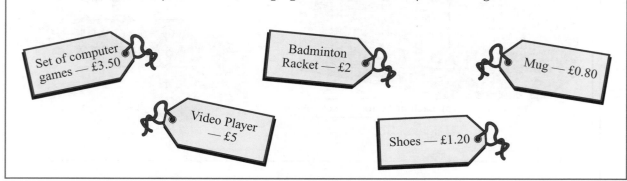

Set of computer games — £3.50

Badminton Racket — £2

Mug — £0.80

Video Player — £5

Shoes — £1.20

a) Melanie decides to **reduce** everything by **15%**. What prices should she write on the labels?

b) Towards the end of the day Melanie is running out of change and decides to round all her prices to the **nearest 10p**. What prices should she write on each of the labels now?

Car Boot Sale

Q5 Jess has made some jewellery and is trying to work out how much to sell each item for.
The receipts for the materials she bought to make the jewellery from are shown below.

Glass beads (large) — £9.65
Glass beads (small) — £6.10
Total — £15.75

10 large red beads   £4
8 small blue beads   £1.60
8 small red beads   £1 60
5 painted beads   £2.50
Total   £9.70

Wire   £4.50
Tongs   £7.60
Total   £12.10
Thank you for shopping at Beaders

a) Jess has made **12 pieces** of jewellery. How much does she need to sell
each piece for to get back the money she has spent on materials?

b) How much would she need to sell each piece for to make a **20% profit**?

c) It took Jess **9 hours** to make all 12 pieces of jewellery. If she sells them all at a **20% profit**,
how much money would she have made for **each hour** she spent making the jewellery?

Q6 Jess also makes wooden sculptures which she sells both at car boot sales and on an online
auction site. The price Jess charges for the sculptures depends on their heights.
The graph below shows the prices of recent sales from car boot sales and the auction site.

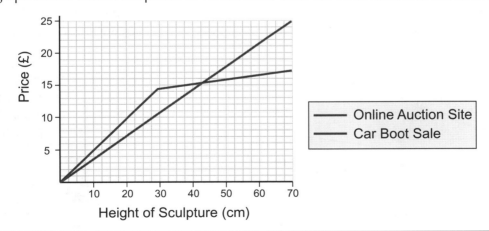

a) Do you think Jess should sell sculptures that are **30 cm** tall
at a car boot sale or online? Explain your answer.

b) Jess has made a sculpture that is **60 cm** tall. How much more money can
she expect to make by selling it at a car boot sale, rather than online?

c) Write a **formula** that Jess can use to calculate the **car boot sale** price of sculptures of **any height**.

Car Boot Sale

Q7 Billy lives in Sitton and is working out which nearby car boot sales he should go to. He has put together the following information.

	Twinton	Crayforth	Wendale	Sitton
Twinton		22	17	15
Crayforth	22		32	12
Wendale	17	32		20
Sitton	15	12	20	

Wendale Events:
Medieval Fayre — 12th June, *free entry*.
Car Boot Sale — 15th June, £3 *entry*.
Barn Dance — 17th June, £6 *entry*.

Car Boot Sale
23rd June
Twinton Town Square
Entry: £5.00

Crayforth Car Boot Sale
19th June, Starts 10am
Entry: £7.50

Petrol: £1.20 per litre

a) On average Billy's car travels **8 miles** for every **litre** of petrol it uses.
Write a **formula** Billy can use for working out the total cost of a trip to a car boot sale.

b) Work out how much money Billy needs to make at **each** car boot sale to cover his **petrol** and **entry costs**.

Q8 Billy's friend Gwen helps him out at a car boot sale in Findale, **17 miles** from Billy's house. At the end of the day they try to sort out their finances. Their notes are shown below.

Billy — owed money for the entry fee and for petrol (car does approx 8 miles per litre).

Petrol: £1.20 per litre

Money in cash box at start of day — £24
Money at end of day — £109.78

Findale Car Boot Sale
Stall holders entry from 7am
Buyers entry from 8am.
Entry Fee: £5.50 per car

Billy leaves a float of **£30** in the cash box, and refunds himself for **entry** and **petrol** costs. He then takes $\frac{2}{3}$ of the remaining money and gives $\frac{1}{3}$ to Gwen. How much do they each receive?

Banking

Q1 Dylan is a student looking to open a bank account. He has **£100** to open the account with. Two high street banks are offering the following deals:

PGS Bank

Amazing deals for students!

Open an account with us today and we will give you **10%** of however much you pay in.

This month you can also get a **third off** *the price of a* **student railcard!** *(Usual price £27).*

Lomond Bank
Investing in Your Future

Calling all students looking for an account.

Look no further — at Lomond Bank we will give you a **quarter** of whatever you pay in to open your account! (Up to a maximum payout of £30)

a) How much would **PGS** pay into Dylan's account?

b) How much would **Lomond Bank** pay into Dylan's account?

c) How much would Dylan **save** on the railcard with PGS Bank?

d) Which bank offers the best introductory deal for Dylan?

Q2 Dylan's dad is encouraging him to save money in his new account.
In January he made him an offer to help him along.

Dylan's 6 Month Challenge!

For each month you pay in at least £20 more than you spend I will give you £10 at the end of the challenge.

And, as an added bonus, I will give you an extra £15 if you manage at least three months.

Good luck!
Dad x

Lomond Bank

Mr D Roberts
A/C 12345678

Month	Paid In	Paid Out
January	£125.00	£96.73
February	£93.45	£52.02
March	£87.60	£69.43
April	£52.85	£36.98
May	£99.76	£48.50
June	£74.50	£106.32

a) In **which months** did Dylan meet his dad's target?

b) **How much money** should Dylan get from his dad at the end of June?

Banking

Q3 Sean earns **£18 000** per year, and has **£10 000** saved up for a deposit on a new flat. He has received a letter from his bank about taking out a mortgage.

> ## PGS Bank
>
> Dear Mr Bourne
>
> Having looked at your finances, I can confirm that we can lend you up to **2.5 times** your salary as a mortgage. This is on the understanding that you are able to pay at least **20%** of the value of the property up front as a deposit. If you wish to discuss this further, please make an appointment to see one of our mortgage advisors.
>
> Yours sincerely
>
> *Dan Le Maison*
>
> Customer Liaison
> PGS Mortgages

a) How much money will the bank lend to Sean based on his present salary?

b) Sean has seen a flat for sale for **£55 000**.
How much more money does he need to save as a deposit for this flat?

Q4 Sean decides to wait until he has saved **£1500** more before he looks for a flat. He sets up a standing order to pay a fixed amount each month from his current account to a new savings account, as shown below.

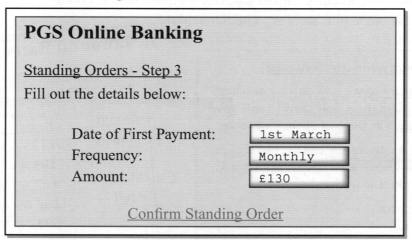

> **PGS Online Banking**
>
> Standing Orders - Step 3
> Fill out the details below:
>
> | | |
> |---|---|
> | Date of First Payment: | 1st March |
> | Frequency: | Monthly |
> | Amount: | £130 |
>
> Confirm Standing Order

a) **How long** will it take Sean to save £1500, if the only money paid into the account is his monthly standing order?

b) After May's payment, Sean decides to increase the monthly amount he saves so he can save £1500 by the end of **November**. What is the minimum he must now save per month to do this?

Banking

Q5 Rebekkah's mum wins some money and puts **£2500** in a savings account for her daughter.

> ### Sharkley's Bank
>
> Dear Mrs Fortune
>
> Thank you for opening a savings account with us.
>
> Interest on this account will be paid every 12 months for as long as you wish to keep the money in the account.
>
> The annual interest rate will be fixed at <u>**4%**</u> for 3 years. You will be advised of any changes after this.
>
> No money can be withdrawn without closing the account. Any interest paid will remain in the account.
>
> We hope you enjoy banking with us.
>
> Yours sincerely
> Fred Sharkley.

a) How much money can Rebekkah expect to be in the savings account after **one year**?

b) Rebekkah decides to leave the money in the account until she leaves school in two years' time. How much will she have in the account after **two years**?

Q6 Emily takes out a loan from Sharkley's Bank to buy a car.
She wants to pay it back in full, plus interest, over **12 months**, in **equal monthly** instalments.

£6750

Typical annual interest rates* for loans with Sharkley's Bank

Amount Borrowed	12 month loan	24 month loan
less than £5000	16.5%	15.5%
£5000 - £10 000	14.5%	13.5%
more than £10 000	12.5%	11.5%

*Interest is calculated at the start of the loan period and added to the total loan amount.

a) How much, **in total**, will Emily have to pay back to the bank?

b) How much will Emily have to pay **each month**, to the nearest penny?

Banking

Q7 Matthew is putting some money into a '5 Year Bond' as an investment for the future.
He is hoping to have a final amount of **£5000**.
Matthew has a formula for working out the amount
he needs to put in the bond, as shown below.

Initial Amount =
Final Amount ÷ 1.05^5

**5 Year Bond
Terms and Conditions**

- _On investing an initial amount of your choice into the bond, you will not be able to pay in or draw out any money for <u>five years</u>._
- _At the end of each year, <u>5%</u> of the total amount in the account will be added on as interest._

Work out the **initial amount** Matthew needs to put in the bond in order to have
a final amount of £5000 after 5 years. Give your answer to the nearest pound.

Q8 Matthew has **£3000** to invest, so his bank
suggests a high interest savings account.

This pays interest at a rate of **4% per year**.

Matthew's friend shows him how to work out the
number of years it will take him to get to £5000:

Hi Matthew
Use this formula:

Final Amount = £3000 × 1.04^n

Keep trying different values
for n, which is the number of
years you'll need to invest for.
Keep going until you get a
final amount of £5000 or more

E.g. After 10 yrs:
Final Amount =
   £3000 × 1.04^{10}
   = £4441 (not enough)

Use trial and improvement to work out **how many years**
it will take Matthew before he has £5000 in this account.